Jip went to the doctor.

The doctor made him better.

3

"I have got a pain in my tail,"
said Deb.
"It has got spots on it."

"Go to the doctor,"
said Ben.
"You are ill."

A pain in the feet

Series editor: Keith Gaines

Illustrated by Tony Kenyon

Nelson

"I have got a pain in my head,"
said Jip.
"I feel sick."

"Go to the doctor,"
said Deb.
"You are ill."

Deb went to the doctor.

The doctor made her better.

"I have got a pain in my legs,"
said Ben.
"I can't stand up."

"Go to the doctor,"
said Meg.
"You are ill."

Ben went to the doctor.

The doctor made him better.

"I have got a pain in my beak,"
said Meg.
"I think I have got a cold."

"Go to the doctor,"
said Sam.
"You are ill."

Meg went to the doctor.

The doctor made her better.

"My teeth hurt,"
said Sam.
"I can't eat my dinner."

"Go to the dentist,"
said Pat.

Sam went to the dentist.

She made his teeth better.

"My feet hurt,"
said Pat.
"I can't walk.
I will have to sit here all day."

"Go to the doctor,"
said Jip.

Pat went to the doctor.

The doctor looked at his feet.

The nurse looked at his feet.

"I don't know why your feet hurt,"
said the doctor.

"I know why your feet hurt,"
said the nurse.
"Your shoes are too small."